I can be good...

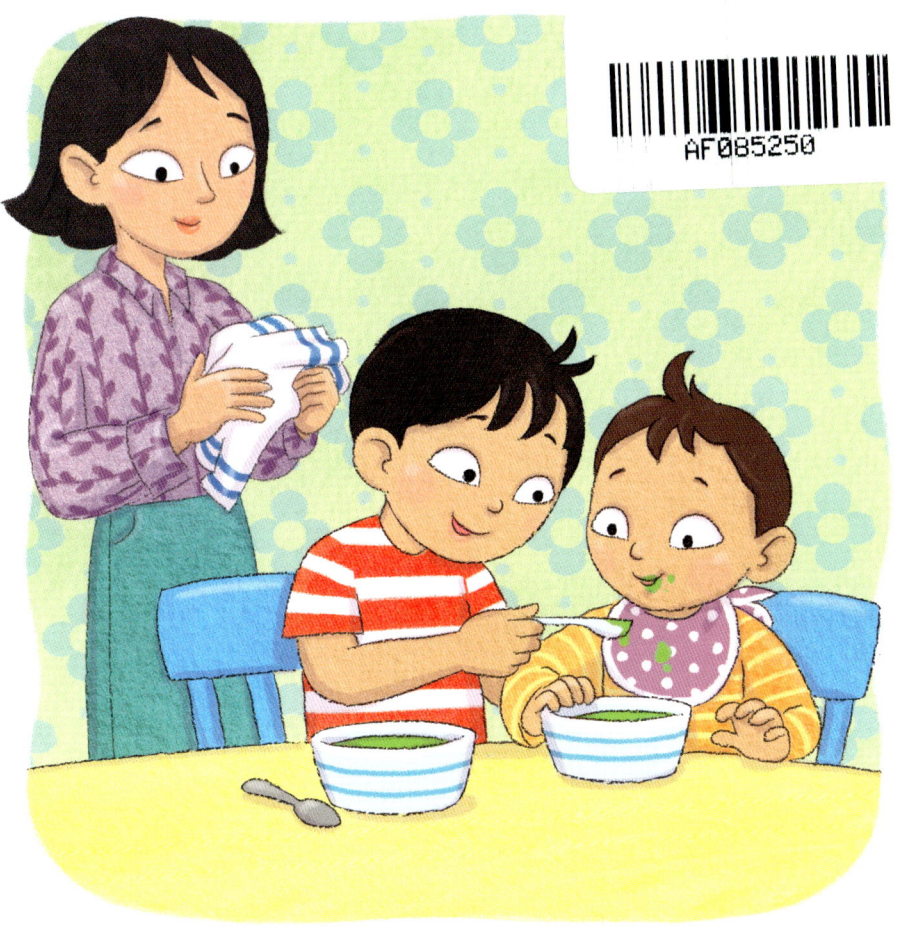

and help!

I can be bad...

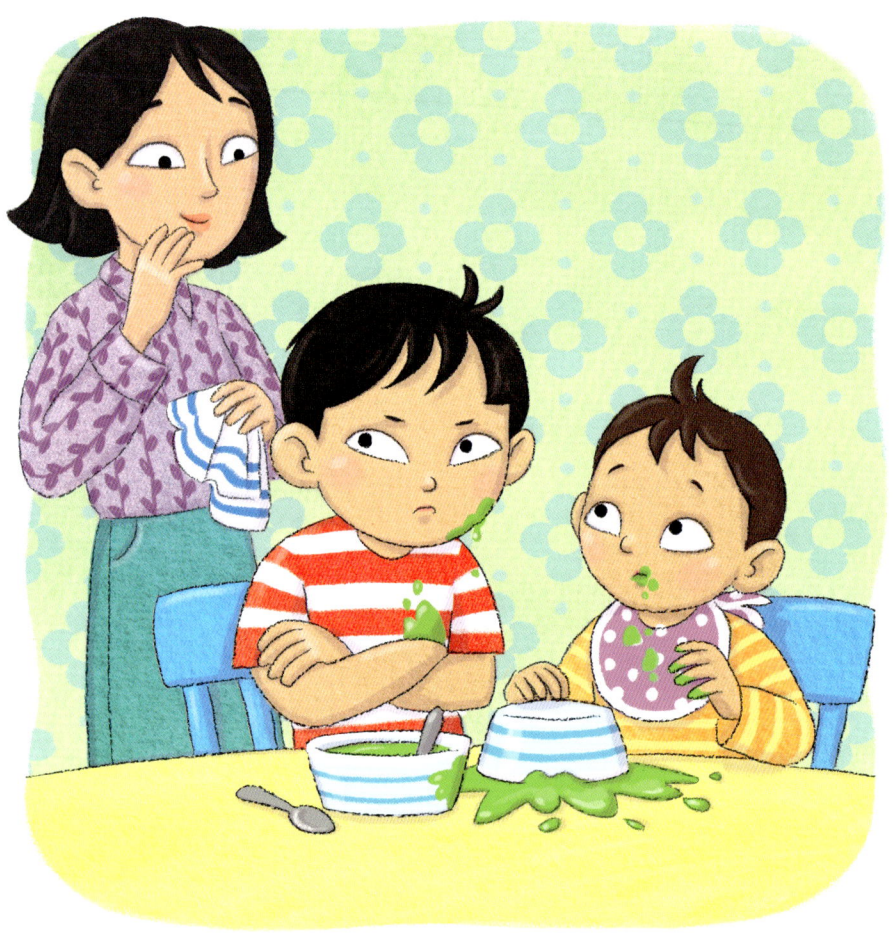

and sulk.

I can be glad...

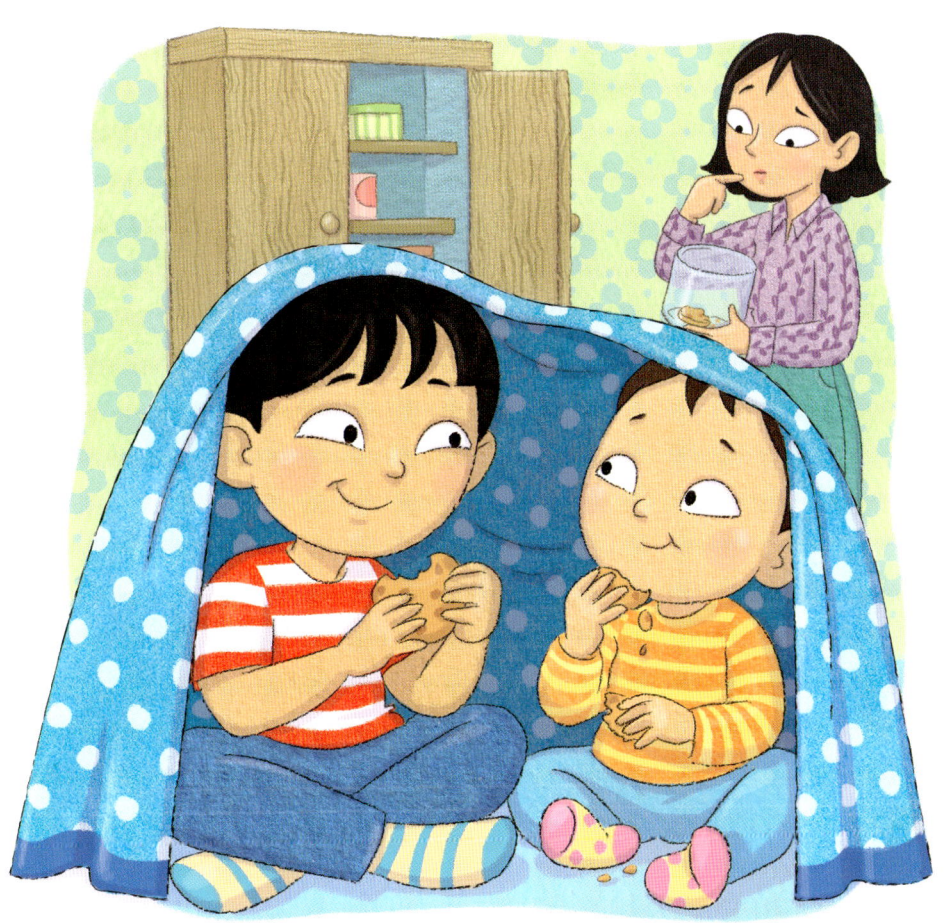

and grin.

I can be sad...

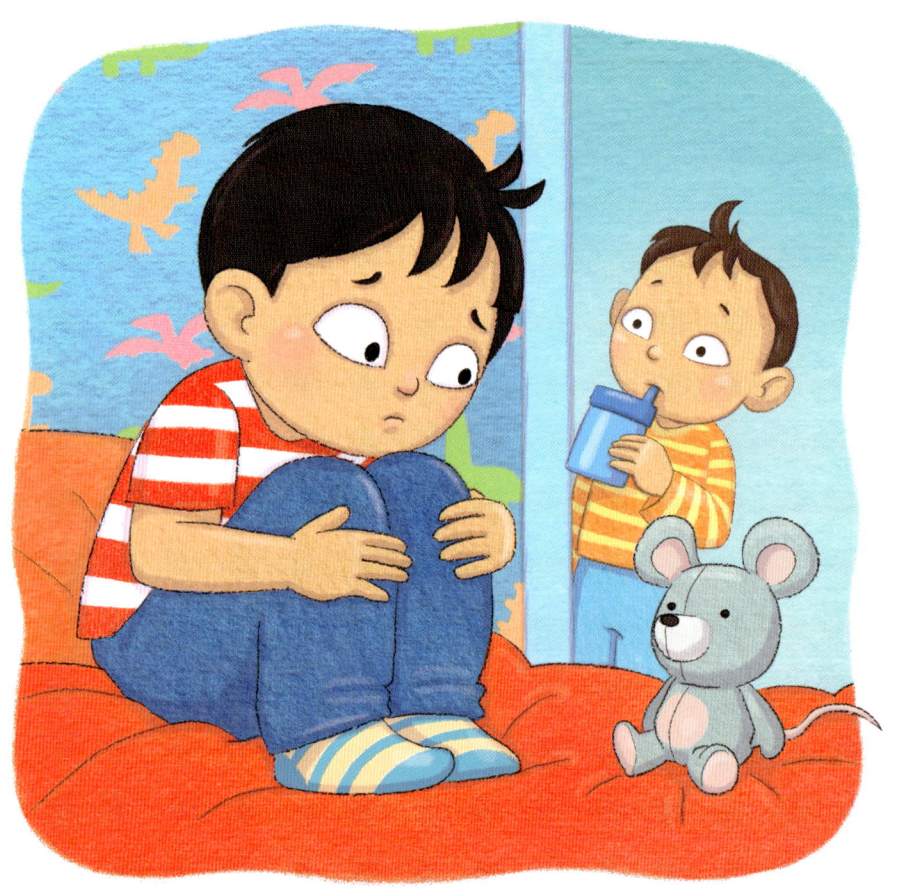

and glum.

I can be cross…

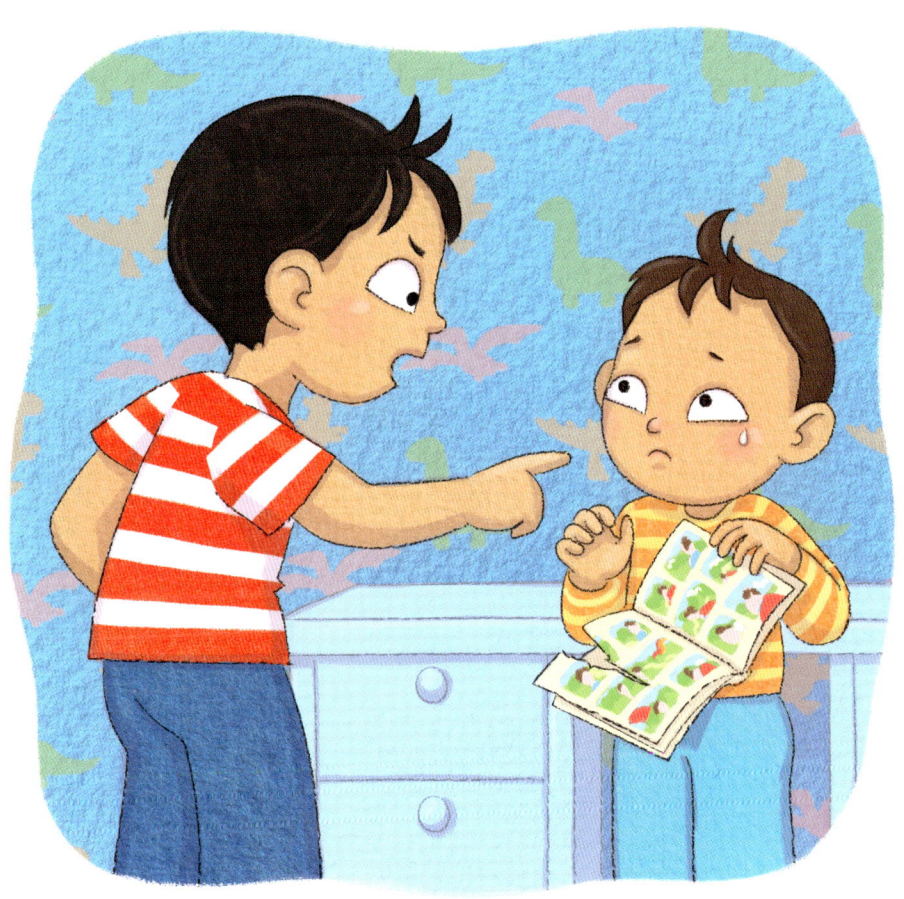

and shout!

I can be fun...

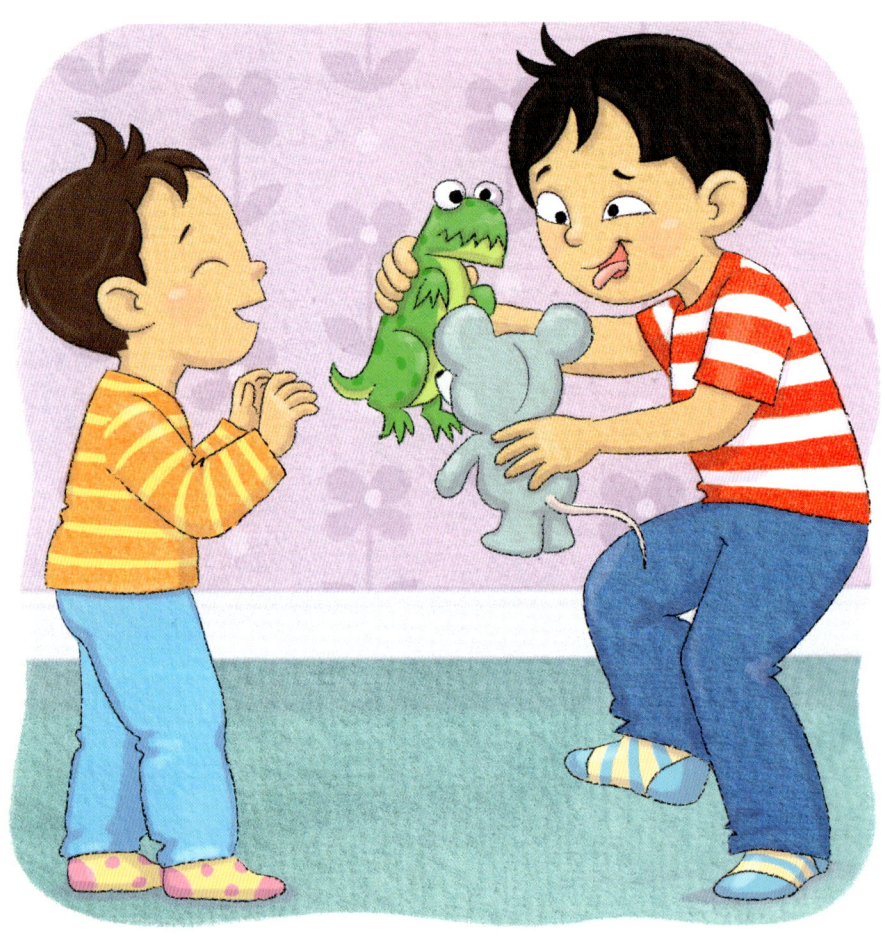

and jest.

I can be...

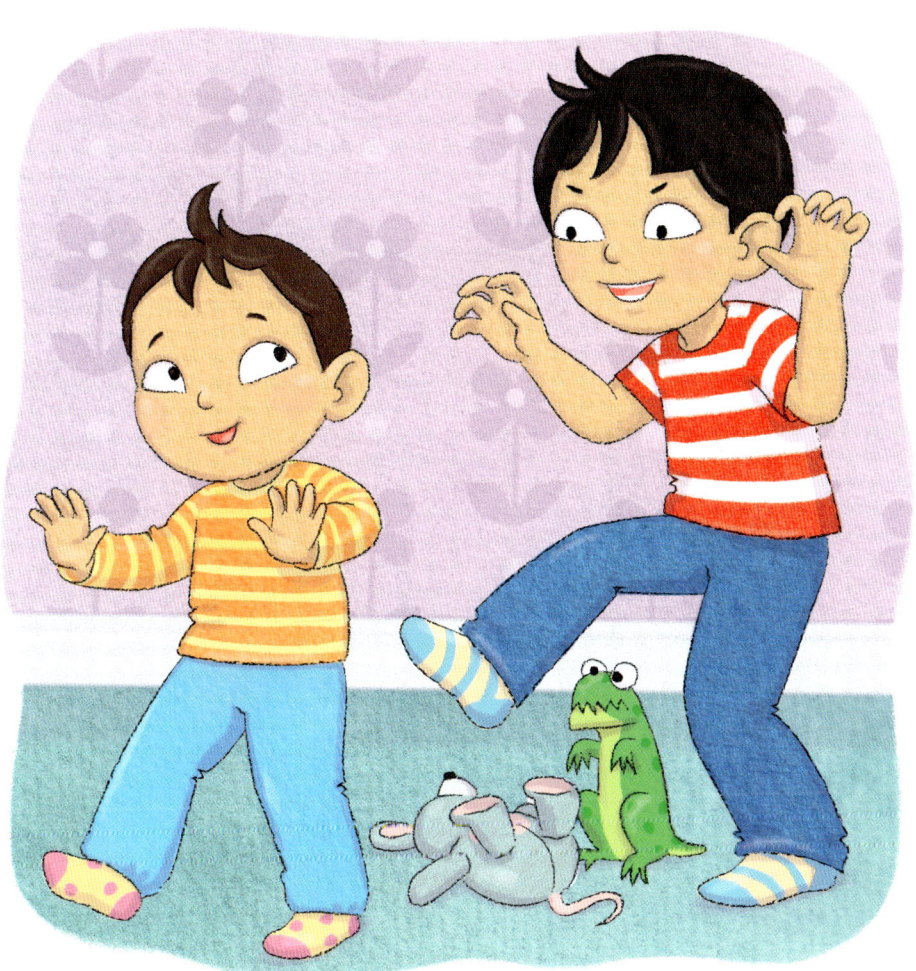

a monster!

I can be... me!

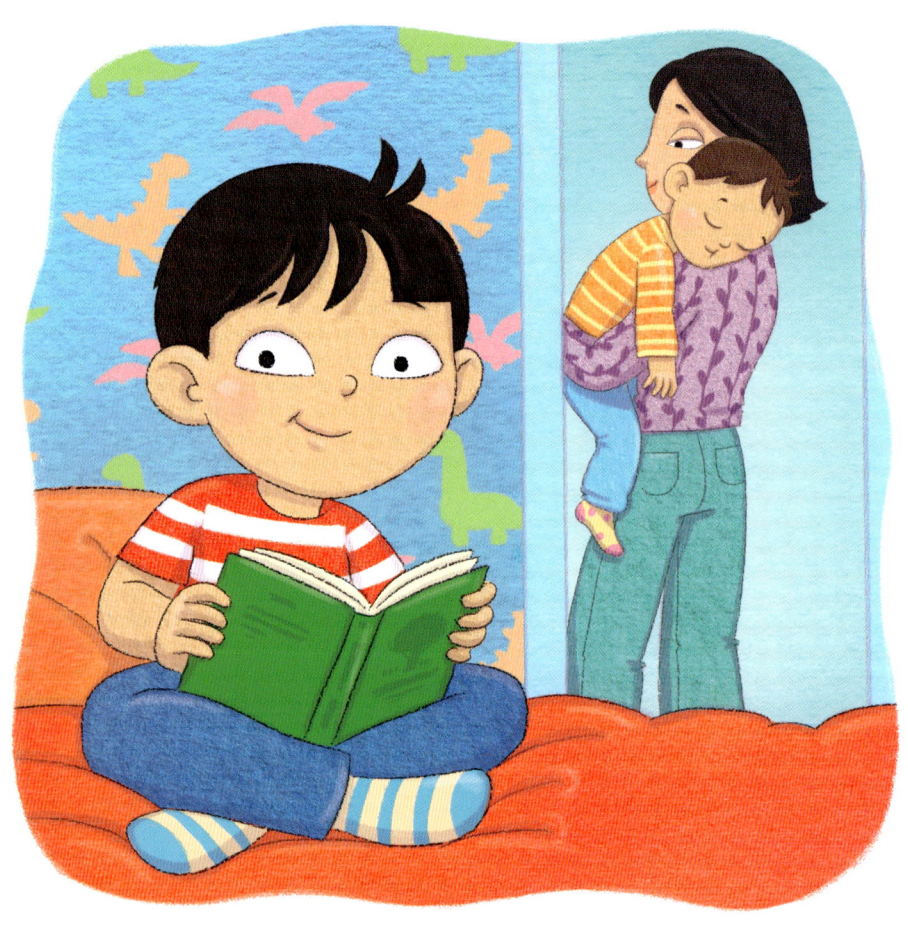

Just me!